Unit 5
Workbook

Skills Strand

GRADE 1

Amplify learning.

ISBN 978-1-61700-204-5

Printed in the USA
09 LSCOW 2021

Unit 5
Workbook

This Workbook contains worksheets that accompany many of the lessons from the *Teacher Guide* for Unit 5. Each worksheet is identified by the lesson number in which it is used. Some of the worksheets in this book do not include written instructions for students because the instructions would have contained undecodable words. The expectation is that teachers will explain these worksheets to the students orally, using the guidelines in the Teacher Guide. The Workbook is a student component, which means each student should have a Workbook.

Name ______________________________

1.1

Dear Family Member,

Today our class started Unit 5 of the Core Knowledge Language Arts program. The Reader for this unit is called *Kate's Book*. Your child will bring home stories you can read together about a young girl named Kate who spends a summer out west with her Nan. Remember that reading at home with your child is important for their success as a reader.

In addition, your child's spelling words for this week include a review of previously taught sound-spellings. As usual, there is one Tricky Word. Tricky Words do not play by the rules, meaning there are spellings that do not sound the way students would expect them to. These words need to be memorized, so your child will benefit from practice reading and writing them.

1. horn
2. porch
3. short
4. park
5. barns
6. herd
7. verb
8. Tricky Word: said

Name ______________________________

1.2

Directions: Have students write each word from the box next to its matching picture. Students should write the words as plural nouns if the picture shows more than one thing.

fan	shark	chick	star	car
dog	horn	ship	spoon	hand

1. ______________________________

2. ______________________________

3. ______________________________

4. ______________________________

5. ______________________________

Directions: Have students write each word from the box next to its matching picture. Students should write the words as plural nouns if the picture shows more than one thing.

fan	shark	chick	star	car
dog	horn	ship	spoon	hand

1. ______________________

2. ______________________

3. ______________________

4. ______________________

5. ______________________

Name ___________________________________

1.3

Can you see the spell·ing patt·ern? Fill in the chart.

Root Word	***–ed* Word**	***–ing* Word**
sip	sipped	sipp·ing
slip		
drop		
clap		
stamp		
hop		
step		
jump		
lap		

Name ______________________

2.1

Directions: Have students look at each picture and label it using the plural or singular form.

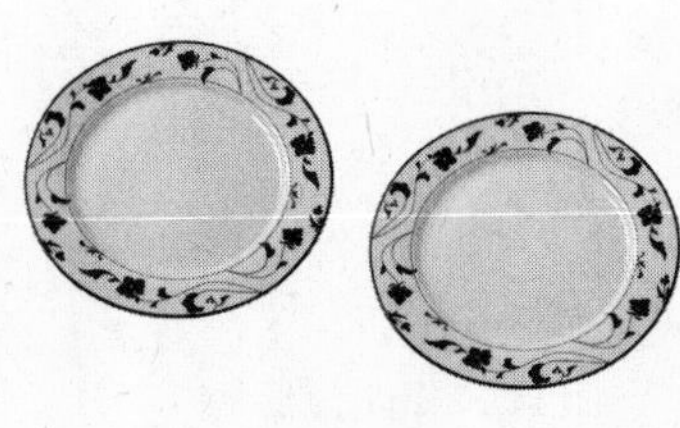

Directions: *Have students look at each picture and label it using the plural or singular form.*

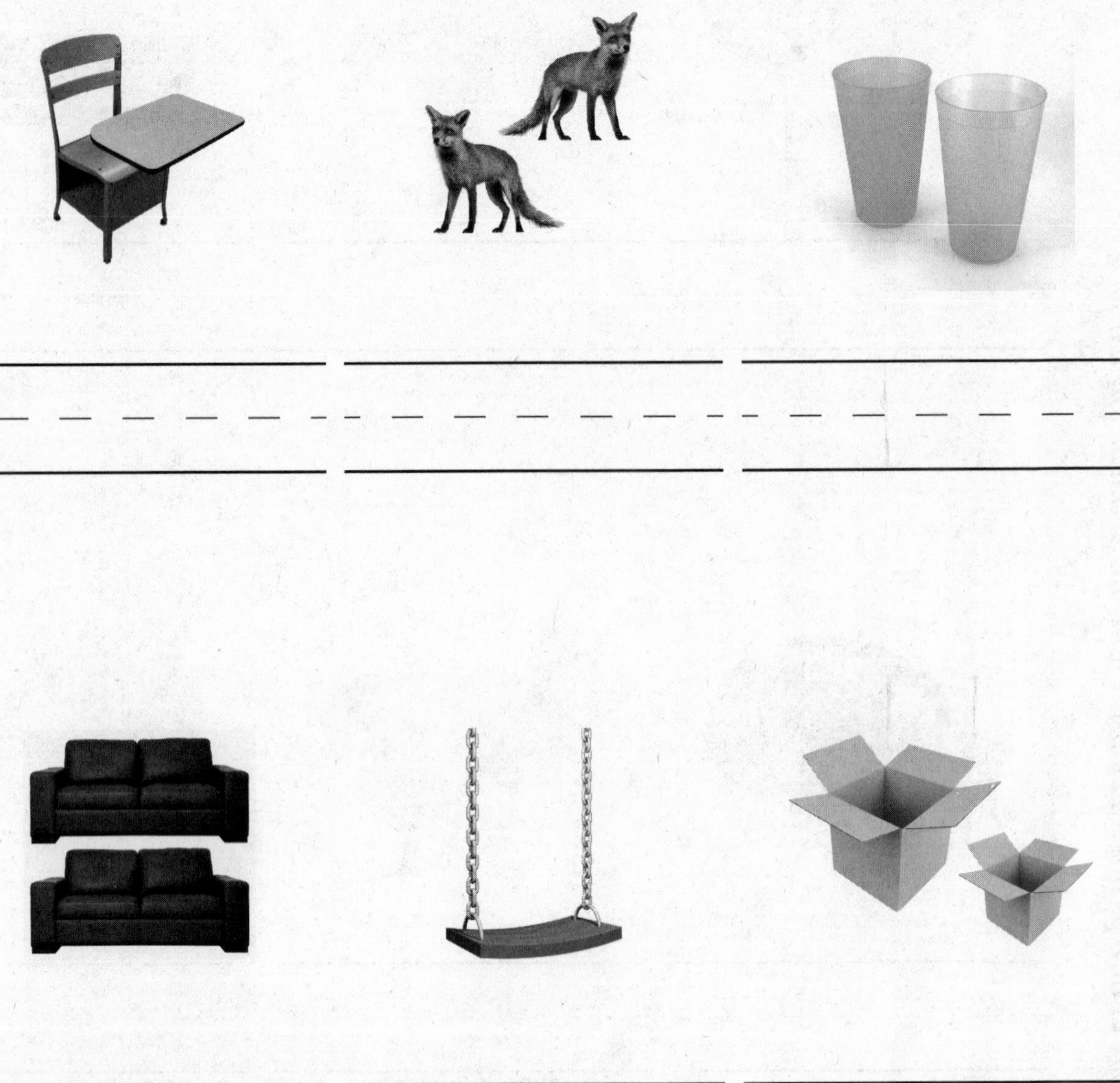

Name ______________________________ **2.2**

A Letter from Kate

1. Who is Nan?

Page ______

2. Where did Kate spend her summ·er?

Page ______

Directions: Have students reread the story and answer the questions.

3. How old was Kate last summ·er?

- ○ Kate was five.
- ○ Kate was nine.
- ○ Kate was ten.

Page ______

4. Kate said that . . .

- ○ Nan made the art.
- ○ Kate made the art.
- ○ Kate's mom made the art.

Page ______

Name ______________________________

3.1

Can you see the spell·ing patt·ern? Fill in the chart.

Root Word	***–ed* Word**	***–ing* Word**
nap	napped	napp·ing
scrub		
stub		
chip		
rob		
grab		
sob		
stop		
pump		
camp		

Name ______________________________

3.2

Directions: Have students trace and copy the punctuation marks. Then have students copy the sentences on the lines, adding the correct ending punctuation.

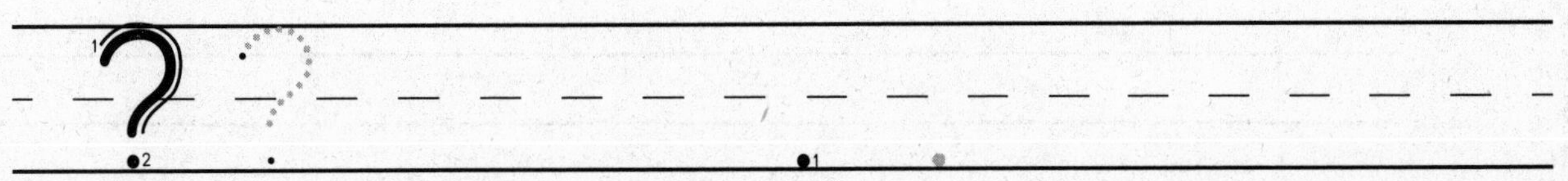

1. The rabb·it ran in·to its hole

2. Where did your dad park his car

Directions: Have students copy the first two sentences on the lines, adding correct ending punctuation. For the sentences below, have students fill in the correct punctuation mark.

3. I add·ed pepp·er to the dish

4. Who add·ed pepp·er to the dish

5. Jen scrubbed the tub [.] ? or .

6. What happ·ened [ ] ? or .

7. Who has a cab·in out west [ ] ? or .

8. Kate went to vis·it her Nan [ ] ? or .

9. Kate made a book [ ] ? or .

10. Who made the art in Kate's book [ ] ? or .

Name ______________________________

3.3

Dear Family Member,

Below is the first story your child has read from a new Reader, *Kate's Book*. Please note that the tricky parts in Tricky Words are underlined in gray, and multi-syllable words are divided between syllables with a dot. This dot serves as a cue to assist students in chunking syllables and will be omitted in later units. Some of the words have been omitted in the version below. Please have your child fill in the blanks using the words from the word box.

After filling in the blanks, ask if your child has any ideas about what fun things Kate may have done with Nan over the summer.

like	art·ist	sad	Skipp·er
summ·er	bor·ing	book	art

A Lett·er from Kate

I'm Kate __________, and this is my book!

This book tells what I did last ____________ when I was nine. My mom and dad took me to vis·it with my Nan. Nan is my mom's mom. She is an ________, and she has a cab·in out in the West.

At the start of my time with Nan, I was sad. It seemed like it would be a _______ summ·er. But in the end I had a lot of fun.

I made this ________ to tell you all the fun stuff I did last summ·er. When I fin·ished it, Nan made the _____. You have the book we made in your hands. I hope you _____ it!

Kate Skipp·er

Name ______________________________

4.1

In the Cave

1. What is the land Kate sees out West like?

   - ○ It is green.
   - ○ It has lots of trees.
   - ○ It has hills and red rocks.

Page __________

2. What was it that Kate and Nan found in the cave?

   - ○ Nan and Kate found a coin.
   - ○ Nan and Kate found a critt·er.
   - ○ Nan and Kate found a rock.

Page __________

Directions: Have students reread the story and answer the questions.

3. What could the coin be made of?

Page

4. What did Nan tell Kate they should do with the coin?

Page

Name ____________________

4.2

Sort the words by their spell·ings for /k/.

cat	king	black	car	skin	book
class	truck	att·ic	fact	like	quack

/k/ → 'c'	/k/ → 'k'	/k/ → 'ck'
cat	king	black

Name ___________________________________ **5.2**

Can you see the spell·ing patt·ern? Fill in the chart.

Root Word	*–ed* Word	*–ing* Word
dab	dabbed	dabb·ing
sip		
ram		
shout		
pound		
look		
duck		
dash		
pop		
mash		
trip		
lick		

Name ______________________________

5.3

Directions: Have students copy the sentences on the lines, adding capital letters at the beginning and the correct punctuation marks at the end.

1. jim likes to splash in the pool in the summ·er

2. which book do you like best

3. would you like one scoop or two scoops

Add . or ? on the lines.

1. The jogg·er ran up the hill ___

2. How late did he get home ___

3. My sis·ter hugged me for a long time ___

4. Where are my slipp·ers ___

5. When did you take a hike in the for·est ___

Name ______________________________

6.1

Spelling Words Lesson 6

1. chips
2. much
3. catch
4. fetch
5. marsh
6. shine
7. flash
8. Tricky Word: how

Name ____ **6.2**

Name ______________________________ **6.3**

kit**ch**·en	chips	scra**tch**
chin	which	ca**tch**

1. ______________ book is it?

2. Dan cooks food in the ______________.

3. Do not ______________ the bug bite!

4. I bumped my ______________.

5. She likes ______________ for a snack.

6. Can you ______________ this?

Directions: Have students complete the sentences with the words from the box.

Name ______________________________

7.1

1. nan drove us to the coin shop

2. are there a lot of coins in that cave

3. jack said that he could sell the coin

Directions: Have students copy the sentences on the lines using correct punctuation.

Directions: Have students write a question and a statement about the picture on the lines below.

Name ______________________________ **7.2**

The Coin Shop

1. What is the coin that Kate found made of?

   - ○ The coin is made of copp·er.
   - ○ The coin is made of sil·ver.
   - ○ The coin is made of steel.

Page ________

2. What sort of coin is it?

   - ○ It is a Du**tch** coin.
   - ○ It is a Brit·ish coin.
   - ○ It is a Span·ish coin.

Page ________

3. Jack said the coin was mint·ed ...

   - ○ in the six·teen hun·dreds.
   - ○ in the nine·teen hun·dreds.
   - ○ last summ·er.

Page ________

Directions: Have students reread the story and answer the questions.

4. If you had a coin that you could sell for three hun·dred bucks, would you keep it or sell it? Why?

Directions: In the box, have students illustrate a part from the story and write a caption below.

Name ________________________________ **7.3**

TAKE HOME

Dear Family Member,

Your child has been learning to read words with the spellings 'ch' (*chin*) and 'tch' (*itch*) for the sound /ch/. The words below contain these spellings. Ask your child to cut out the word cards. Show the cards to your child to read aloud and use in a sentence. Your child can sort the words into piles according to which spelling is used for /ch/. There are also Tricky Words which are marked with an *.

ki**tch**·en	ca**tch**·er	chips	should*
stre**tch**	chin	ba**tch**	sti**tch**·es
ha**tch**	march	how*	fe**tch**ed
much	be·cause*	scra**tch**·ing	chant

Name ______________________________

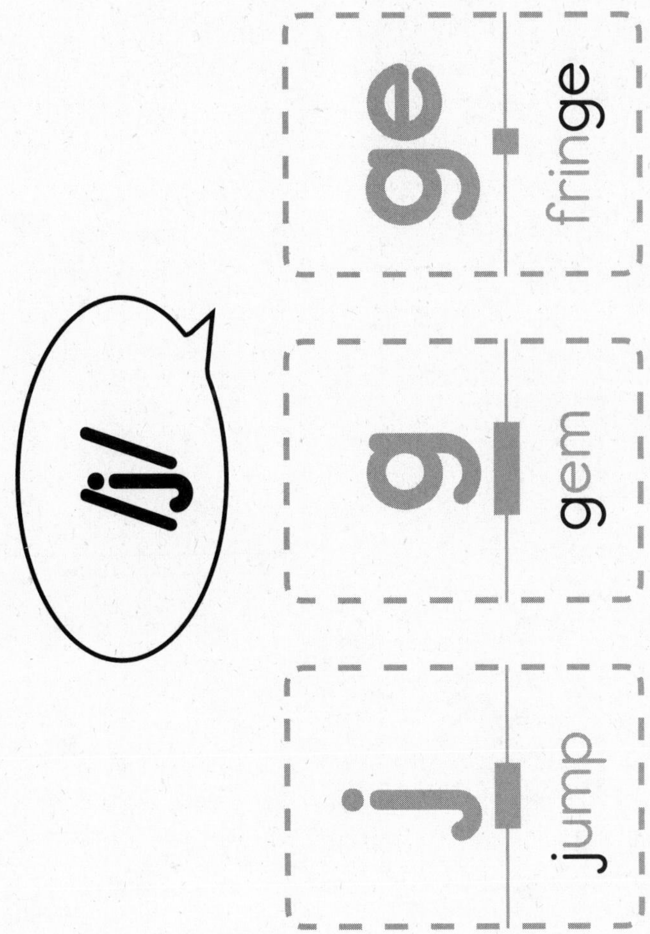

Name ______________________________

8.2

You Never Can Tell

1. Nan said Kate had to sell the coin.

 ○ yes

 ○ no

2. Kate did sell the coin.

 ○ yes

 ○ no

3. Kate and Nan think that a robb·er could have hidd·en the coin in the cave.

 ○ yes

 ○ no

4. Things that are rare cost a lot.

 ○ yes

 ○ no

Directions: Have students reread the story and choose the correct answer.

5. Is Kate glad that she found the coin? Why or why not?

Directions: *In the box, have students illustrate a part of the story and write a caption below.*

Name ______________________________

8.3

Dear Family Member,

This is a story from the Reader *Kate's Book*. Encourage your child to read the story to you and then talk about it together. The tricky parts in Tricky Words are underlined in gray. Please note that multi-syllable words are divided between syllables with a dot. This dot serves as a cue to assist students in chunking syllables and will be omitted in later units.

Repeated reading is an important way to improve reading. It can be fun for your child to repeatedly read this story to a friend, relative, or even a pet.

The Coin Shop

Nan drove us to the coin shop.

The man in the coin shop was a pal of hers. His name was Jack.

"Jack," Nan said, "this is Kate Skipp·er. I'm Kate's nan. She's out here for the summ·er. We went for a hike, and Kate found a coin in a cave."

"Well, Miss Skipp·er," Jack said, "let's have a look at it!"

I hand·ed him the coin.

Jack set it un·der a look·ing glass and swi**tch**ed on a lamp. "Let's see," he said. "It's got some scra**tch**·es on it. But I can tell that it's a Span·ish coin. It's made of sil·ver, too."

"When was it made?" asked Nan.

"There's no date on the coin," said Jack. "But I'll bet it dates back to the six·teen hun·dreds. The Span·ish mint·ed a big ba**tch** of coins like this one back then."

"Good·ness!" said Nan.

"Is that a long time back in the past?" I asked.

"Yes," said Jack. "Let me run and fe**tch** my book on Span·ish coins."

When Jack came back, he said, "There's just one thing I need you to tell me, Miss Skipp·er."

"What's that?" I asked.

"Are there a lot of coins like this one in that cave?"

"No," I said, "we found just this one."

"That's a shame," Jack said.

"Why?" I asked.

"If there were a lot of coins, you and your Nan would be rich!" said Jack. "I could sell a coin like this for three hun·dred bucks!"

"Three hun·dred bucks?" said Nan.

Jack nodd·ed.

"Yipp·ee!" I shout·ed. "I'm rich!"

Name ____________________

9.1

Sound out the words with the lines un·der them. Is the 'g' sound·ed /g/ as in *got* or /j/ as in *gem*? Print the words where they fit.

1	g	2
gum		gem
glad		germ
dog		

	/g/ as in *got*	/j/ as in *gem*
1. A cat is larg·er than a rat.		larger
2. We have two arms and two legs.		
3. Can germs make you sick?		
4. I'd rath·er ride my bike than jog.		
5. There are plants in the gar·den.		

Name ______________________

The Offer

1. What was Jack's off·er?
   - ○ His off·er was to take the coin.
   - ○ His off·er was to take Nan and Kate camp·ing.
   - ○ His off·er was to make dinn·er.

Page ______

2. To Kate, camp·ing sounds like . . .
   - ○ fun.
   - ○ it would be bor·ing.
   - ○ a hard time.

Page ______

Directions: Have students read the story and answer the questions.

3. What will Kate, Nan, Jack, and Max do on their camp·ing trip?

Page ____________

4. Will Kate sleep in a bed or sleep in a tent?

Page ____________

Name ______________________________ **9.3**

Dear Family Member,

Your child has been learning about how to form plural nouns. In class, we have been listening to the sound that 's' makes at the end of a word. For *books*, for example, the 's' makes a /s/ sound, whereas the word *dogs* has the buzzy /z/ sound. Below are a number of words your child should change to the plural form. Ask your child to listen for either the /s/ or /z/ sound at the end. Have students place their fingers on their voice boxes so they can feel the difference between /s/ and /z/. Remind your child that when a word ends in 'sh', 'ch', 's', and 'x', we add 'es' to change it to the plural form.

one book	five books
one splash	three ______
one ma**tch**	nine ______
one fox	ten ______
one dog	five ______
one chimp	two ______
one dish	nine ______
one box	three ______
one buck	ten ______
one spoon	two ______

Name ______________________________ **10.1**

Spelling Test

1. ______________________________

2. ______________________________

3. ______________________________

4. ______________________________

5. ______________________________

6. ______________________________

7. ______________________________

8. ______________________________

Name ____________________ **10.2**

The Campsite

1. Jack picked Kate and Nan up in his . . .

○ car.

○ cab.

○ truck.

Page ________

2. The Bad·lands are good for . . .

○ camp·ing.

○ farm·ing.

○ swimm·ing.

Page ________

3. What did Kate un·pack at the camp·site?

○ She un·packed sleep·ing bags and tents.

○ She un·packed tents and games.

○ She un·packed sleeping bags and games.

Page ________

Directions: Have students read the story and answer the questions.

Directions: Have students retell the end of the story or copy his or her favorite sentences from the end of the story.

Name ______________________________

11.1

TAKE HOME

Dear Family Member,

Our class has been continuing to read and write two-syllable words. Your child may find it helpful to practice writing and remembering the spelling words syllable by syllable. The spelling words this week all have the /j/ sound. The /j/ sound can be written with the spellings 'j', 'g', and 'ge'.

Spelling Words Lesson 11

1. jumping
2. jars
3. germ
4. gem
5. charged
6. fringe
7. magic
8. Tricky Word: your

Name ____________________

11.2

Sort the words by their spell·ings for /t/.

time	un·til	sit	truck
cut	baked	bitt·er	cutt·ing
parked	sitt·ing	ripped	hoped

/t/ → 't'	/t/ → 'tt'	/t/ → 'ed'

Can you see the spell·ing patt·ern? Fill in the chart.

Root Word	***–er* Word**	***–est* Word**
wet	wett·er	wett·est
hot		
short		
fit		
round		

Name ______________________

11.3

! ! ? ? . .

1. nan, what is that ☐

2. that sounds like fun ☐

3. what sort of coin is it ☐

4. it is a Span·ish coin ☐

Directions: Have students first read each sentence to determine which ending punctuation should be added in the box. Then have students rewrite the sentence to include correct punctuation and capitalization.

5. when was the coin made ☐

6. the coin is from the six·teen hun·dreds ☐

7. "Yippee ☐ " I shout·ed.

8. I am rich ☐

Name ______________________________

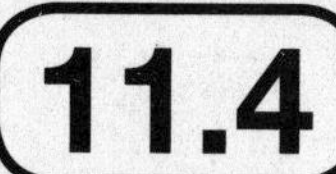

Dear Family Member,

Your child has been learning to read words with the spellings 'tch' as in *catch* and 'ge' as in *merge*. Have your child cut out the word cards. Show the cards to your child, and have your child read them and use them in a sentence. Ask your child to copy the words onto a sheet of paper. You may also read the words out loud and have your child write the words down, one sound at a time. Please keep the cards for future practice.

ca**tch**	lar**ge**	bul**ge**
ha**tch**	bar**ge**	ki**tch**·en
char**ge**	plun**ge**	scra**tch**
mer**ge**	i**tch**	ke**tch**·up

Name ______________________

12.1

Sort the words by their spell·ings for /d/.

down	could	duck	add
trimmed	shred	shredd·ing	wedd·ing
odd	hide	said	planned

/d/ → 'd'	**/d/ → 'dd'**	**/d/ → 'ed'**

Can you see the spell·ing patt·ern? Fill in the chart.

Root Word	*–er* Word	*–est* Word
mad	madd·er	madd·est
sad		
hard		
red		
loud		

Name ______________________________

12.2

Jack's Tale

1. What did Jack do af·ter dinn·er?

   - ○ Jack went to bed af·ter dinn·er.
   - ○ Jack shared a tale af·ter dinn·er.
   - ○ Jack went home af·ter dinn·er.

Page __________

2. Who was Bart?

   - ○ Bart was a robb·er who took hors·es.
   - ○ Bart was a robb·er who took cars.
   - ○ Bart was a robb·er who robbed the stage·coach.

Page __________

3. What sort of mann·ers did Bart have?

   - ○ Bart had bad mann·ers.
   - ○ Bart had so-so mann·ers.
   - ○ Bart had good mann·ers.

Page __________

Directions: Have students reread the story and answer the questions.

4. What is a strong·box?

Page

5. What happ·ened to Bart af·ter he was nabbed?

Page

Name ______________________________

12.3

Dear Family Member,

Your child has been learning to read words with the spellings 'ch' (*chin*) and 'tch' (*itch*) for the sound /ch/ and the spelling alternatives 'j' (*jump*), 'g' (*germ*), and 'ge' (*large*) for the sound /j/. The words below contain these spellings. Ask your child to cut out the word cards. Show the cards to your child, and have your child read them. Extension: Have your child sort the words into piles according to which spellings are used for the sounds /ch/ and /j/.

chase	hin**ge**	**g**erm
ma**tch**	sna**tch**	pi**tch**
swi**tch**	jaw	much
gem	lun**ge**	jack·et

Name ______________________

13.1

muff·ins	**g**in·**g**er	af·ter	sta**ge**·coach
off	le**g**·end	traff·ic	ma**tch**·es

1. Will you munch on ______________ snaps af·ter dinn·er?

2. We were late be·cause of ______________.

3. James made ______________ to share with his pals.

4. I can go to·day ______________ class.

muff·ins	**g**in·**g**er	af·ter	sta**ge**·coach
off	le**g**·end	traff·ic	ma**tch**·es

5. Out·laws robbed the ____________________.

6. I must get __________ the bus!

7. Nan shared a __________ with us.

8. Do you need __________ for the fire?

Name ______________________________ **13.2**

Directions: Have students read the sentences to determine which punctuation to add to the first five items. Students should then create their own questions, exclamations, and statements.

1. The kitt·en sleeps ☐

2. I can't sleep because my bug bites itch ☐

3. Will the chicks hatch soon ☐

4. Do not yell ☐

5. Roger can cook ☐

6. ______________________________?

7. ______________________________!

8. ______________________________.

Name ______________________________ **13.3**

The Visit

Fill in the ____ with words from the box.

tree	pots and pans	~~pack~~
tents	lan·tern	

1. They stuffed the food in·to a lar**ge** pack.

2. They kept the food pack up in a ____________.

3. They all went to sleep in th<u>eir</u> ____________.

4. The loud clatt·er of ____________ woke them up.

5. To see in the dark, they used a ____________.

6. Why did Jack hoist the food up in the tree?

Page

7. Draw one of the parts of "The Vis·it."

Name ______________________________

14.1

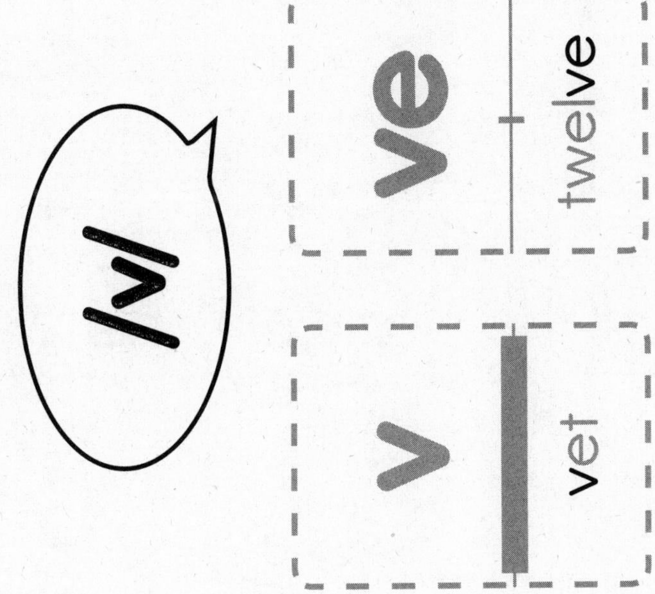

Name ______________________________

14.2

verbs	van	ser**ve**	riv·er
twel**ve**	vote	nev·er	vet

1. Run and jump are ______________.

2. When I was ______________, I went to camp.

3. She will ______________ you a big snack.

4. We took the dog to the ______________.

Directions: Have students complete the sentences with the words from the box.

verbs	van	ser**ve**	riv·er
twel**ve**	vote	nev·er	vet

5. I went swimm·ing in the ___________.

6. You ___________ can tell!

7. Will you ___________ for me?

8. Can we drive to the park in the ___________?

Directions: Have students complete the sentences with the words from the box.

Name ______________________________ **14.3**

The Hike

1. When did Max and Kate dig up the bone?

   ○ Max and Kate dug up the bone in the morn·ing.

   ○ Max and Kate dug up the bone af·ter lunch.

   ○ Max and Kate dug up the bone af·ter dinn·er.

Page ________

2. What did Max and Kate use to dig out the bone?

   ○ Max and Kate used forks.

   ○ Max and Kate used spoons.

   ○ Max and Kate used hamm·ers.

Page ________

3. How long was the bone?

   ○ The bone was one foot long.

   ○ The bone was two feet long.

   ○ The bone was three feet long.

Page ________

Directions: Have students reread the story and answer the questions.

4. Who needs to look at the bone to tell Max and Kate the sort of bone it is?

Page ____________

Name ____________________

14.4

Dear Family Member,

This is a story your child has probably read once, possibly several times, at school. Encourage your child to read the story to you and then talk about it together. The tricky parts in Tricky Words are underlined in gray. Please note that multi-syllable words are divided between syllables with a dot. This dot serves as a cue to assist students in chunking syllables and will be omitted in later units.

Repeated reading is an important way to improve reading. It can be fun for your child to repeatedly read this story to a friend, relative, or even a pet.

The Campsite

Jack came and picked us up in his truck. We drove to a camp·site in the Bad·lands.

"Nan," I said, "what's up with that name—the Bad·lands?"

"Well," said Nan, "le**g**·end has it that a long time back, farm·ers came out here look·ing for farm·land. When they saw all of the rocks and sand and stone, they said, 'This is bad land! We can't plant crops here!' And the name Bad·lands just sort of stuck."

"It's bad land for farm·ing," said Jack. "But it's good land for camp·ing!"

When we got to the camp·site, we had to un·pack sleep·ing bags, tents, lan·terns, ma**tch**·es, and lots of food. We lugged it all to the camp·site.

Jack chose a spot to set up camp. Max and I helped set up the tents. It took us a long time.

For dinn·er we had hot dogs. We stuck them on sticks and held them in the fire. My hot dog got all black be·cause I left it in there too long. Max gave me one of his.

That was when I said to my·self, "Max is OK!"

Name ______________________

15.1

Spelling Test

1. ______________________

2. ______________________

3. ______________________

4. ______________________

5. ______________________

6. ______________________

7. ______________________

8. ______________________

Name ____________________

15.2

The Best Book Ever

The best book ev·er is called *The Green Fern Zoo*. In the book, a zoo keep·er named Vern takes chil·dren in to see the zoo and meet all of the critt·ers. I like this book a lot be·cause Vern tells lots of fun facts that des·cribe all of the critt·ers. The snap·shots are fan·tas·tic be·cause they make you feel like you are in the zoo and close to the critt·ers. You should pick up *The Green Fern Zoo* be·cause it is a book you will not for·get!

Name ____

16.1

Dear Family Member,

Our class has been reading stories from *Kate's Book*. Your child can tell you about the adventures Kate has been having with Nan and their friends Jack and Max. Remember that reading at home with your child is important for their success as a reader.

The spelling words for this week contain the /t/, /d/, and /f/ sounds. Your child can practice reading and writing these words, as well as clap the syllables for them. The last spelling word is a Tricky Word. Tricky Words do not play by the rules, meaning there are spellings that do not sound the way students would expect them to. These words need to be memorized.

Spelling Words Lesson 16

1. trucker
2. kitten
3. parked
4. duck
5. add
6. planned
7. offer
8. Tricky Word: was

Name ____ **16.2**

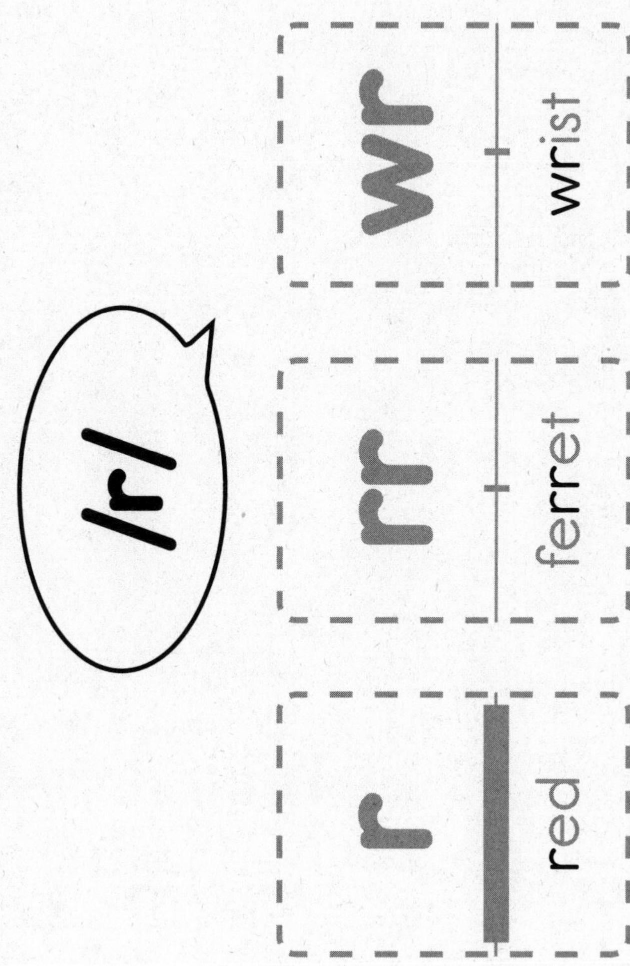

Name ____________________

16.3

Directions: Have students read the sentence and circle the spellings that stand for the /r/ sound. At the end of each sentence is the amount of times the /r/ sound occurs.

The box had red wrapp·ing on it. (2)

red wrapping

1. I like to vis·it the rep·tile room. (2)

2. They wrapped my cast in the wrong fab·ric. (3)

3. I got a ride up the ramp. (2)

4. My name is writt·en in the book. (1)

5. I took a long trip with my pal Rex. (2)

6. We hiked on the red rocks. (2)

7. I am not wrong! (1)

8. Do not wreck the room! (2)

Name ____________________

17.1

Take a Stand and Tell Why (Plan)

Take a Stand on *Kate's Book*	
Des·cribe *Kate's Book*	
Tell Why #1	
Tell Why #2	
End with a Zing·er	

Name

17.2

Take a Stand and Tell Why (Draft)

Date:

Dear Kate,

Cheers,

Name ______________________________ **17.3**

The Bone Man

1. Who is Ron Fi**tch**?

   ○ Ron Fi**tch** is a pal of Nan's.

   ○ Ron Fi**tch** is an ex·pert on coins.

   ○ Ron Fi**tch** is an ex·pert on bones.

Pa**g**e __________

2. What did Max tell Kate a T. rex is?

   ○ The T. rex is the bigg·est and fast·est in·sect of all time.

   ○ The T. rex is the cool·est, bigg·est rep·tile of all time.

   ○ The T. rex is the bigg·est and fast·est dog of all time.

Pa**g**e __________

3. Which word is the noun in "the cool·est, bigg·est rep·tile"?

____

____

Directions: Have students reread the story and answer the questions.

4. Why is it so cool that Kate and Max found a T. rex bone?

Page

5. What should Kate and Max do with the T. rex bone?

Name ______________________________ **17.4**

Dear Family Member,

Please have your child complete the sentences with the words from the box.

morn·ing	bigg·est	stre**tch**ed	ki**tch**·en
scra**tch**·ing	lar**ge**	rocks	ba**tch**

1. Out West there are hills and red ____________.

2. We went for a hike in the ____________.

3. We dug up a ____________ bone that was three feet long.

4. It was the ____________ bone I had ev·er seen!

morn·ing	bigg·est	stre**tch**ed	ki**tch**·en
scra**tch**·ing	lar**ge**	rocks	ba**tch**

5. I can't stop ______________ my bug bite!

6. Is Dad cook·ing in the ______________?

7. I made a big ______________ of sweets!

8. I ______________ out my arms to get the book.

Name ____________________

18.1

Check the Draft Step by Step

Step	Check?
Check that the date is there.	
Check that "Dear Kate" is there.	
Check that you took a stand on *Kate's Book*.	
Check that you des·cribed *Kate's Book*.	
Did you Tell Why #1 with be·cause?	
Did you Tell Why #2 with be·cause?	
Check that you end·ed the lett·er with a zing·er.	
Check that you closed the lett·er and gave your name.	
Aa, Bb, Cc and ? . !	
Check that the words are spelled well.	

Name ____ **18.2**

Dear Family Member,

This is a story your child has probably read once, possibly several times, at school. Encourage your child to read the story to you and then talk about it together. The tricky parts in Tricky Words are underlined in gray. Please note that multi-syllable words are divided between syllables with a dot. This dot serves as a cue to assist students in chunking syllables and will be omitted in later units.

Repeated reading is an important way to improve reading. It can be fun for your child to repeatedly read this story to a friend, relative, or even a pet.

The Visit

Af·ter tell·ing us the tale, Jack said, "It's time to pack up the food."

We stuffed the food in·to a lar**ge** pack with a rope on it. Jack tossed the rope up in·to a tree and hoist·ed the food pack up so that it was hang·ing ten feet off of the ground.

"Paw-paw," said Max, "why do we have to keep the food up in the tree?"

"Be·cause it will keep the food safe from fox·es and racc·oons that would like to snack on it," Jack said.

Af·ter that, we crawled in·to the tents, flipped off our lan·terns, and went to sleep.

Nan and I slept well un·til a loud clatt·er out·side woke us up.

"What was that?" I asked.

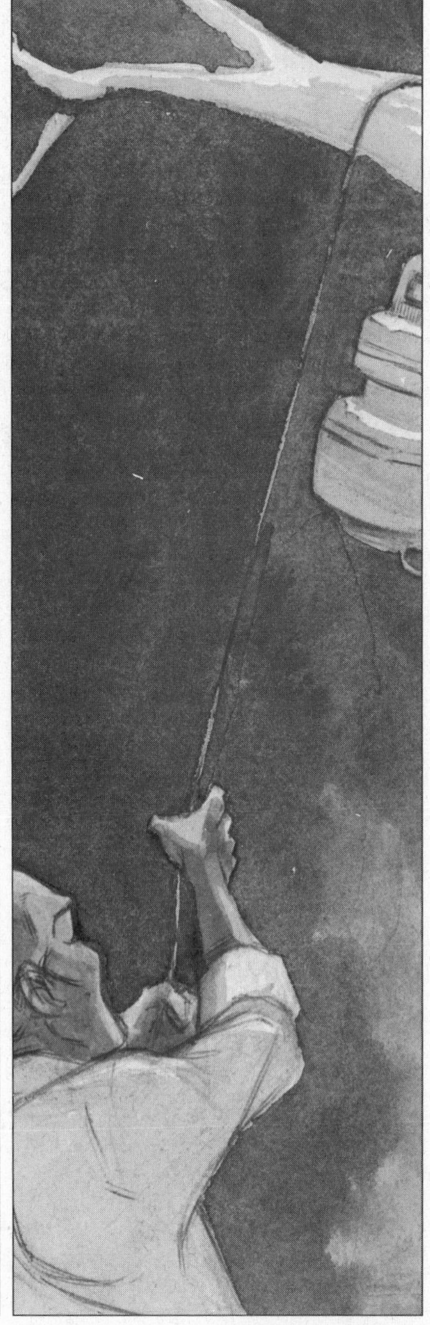

"I can't tell," said Nan, as she hugged me close to her.

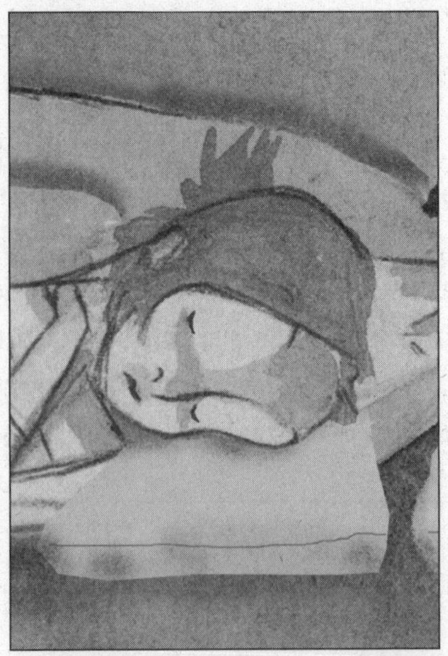

Jack ran out·side with his lan·tern and yelled, "Get out of here! Scram! Get lost!"

When we went out, we saw Jack and Max stand·ing there. Jack had his lan·tern.

"Jack," Nan asked, "who came to vis·it?"

"I did not see it," said Jack, "but I'm bett·ing it was a fox who was look·ing for some scraps of food. He bumped in·to the pots and pans. The clatt·er of the pots and pans must have scared him off."

"Is that why we hoist·ed the food pack up in the tree?" Max asked.

"That's why!" said Jack.

Name ______________________________

Sort the words by their spell·ings for /l/.

long	like	lar**ge**
sol**ve**	all	smell
look	slee**ve**	well
still	la**tch**	skill

/l/ → 'l'	**/l/ → 'll'**
______________	______________
______________	______________
______________	______________
______________	______________
______________	______________
______________	______________
______________	______________
______________	______________

Name ________________________________

Two Good Things and One Bad Thing

1. What sort of bone did Max and Kate dig up?

Page ________

2. Why can't Max and Kate keep the bone?

Page ________

Directions: Have students reread the story and answer the questions.

3. What will Ron Fi**tch** do next?

Pa**g**e ____________

4. What name would you pick for the T. rex? Why?

Name ____ **20.3**

Dear Family Member,

This is a story your child has probably read once, possibly several times, at school. Encourage your child to read the story to you and then talk about it together. The tricky parts in Tricky Words are underlined in gray. Please note that multi-syllable words are divided between syllables with a dot. This dot serves as a cue to assist students in chunking syllables and will be omitted in later units.

Repeated oral reading is an important way to improve reading. It can be fun for your child to repeatedly read this story to a friend, relative, or even a pet.

The Hike

The next morn·ing, we went on a hike. Af·ter a bit, we stopped for lunch.

When Max fin·ished his lunch, he asked, "Can Kate and I look for rocks?"

Jack said OK.

"Kate," Max said to me, "bring your fork. We can use it to dig up rocks."

I grabbed my fork, and we went off to look for rocks.

Max point·ed at a bump on the side of a cliff and said, "Let's dig that rock out!"

The rock did not look all that lar**ge**. But when we start·ed digg·ing, we soon saw that it was lar**g**·er than it had seemed.

Af·ter a bit, Max said, "**G**ee! It must be two feet long! We need to keep scra**tch**·ing in or·der to car**ve** it out of the side of the cliff."

We went on scra**tch**·ing with our forks.

"Let's tug on it!" Max said "I bet we can get it out by our·sel**ve**s."

We grabbed and tugged it.

It popped out. But so did a big cloud of sand and dust. Max and I fell down.

Once the dust and sand had drift·ed off, I saw Max stand·ing there with the thing in his hands.

"It's not a rock!" he yelled. "It's a bone!"

It was the bigg·est bone I had ev·er seen. It was three feet long!

Jack and Nan came runn·ing.

"Good·ness!" said Nan. "That is one lar**ge** bone! Where did you get it?"

Max point·ed to the spot where we found it.

Jack set the bone on the ground. Then he took a pic·ture of the bone and said, "We need to get an ex·pert to look at this bone and tell us what sort of bone it is."

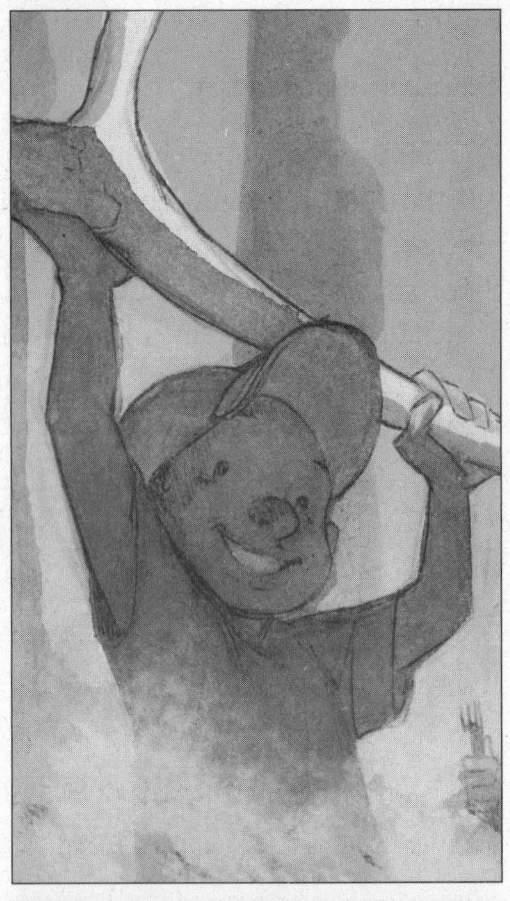

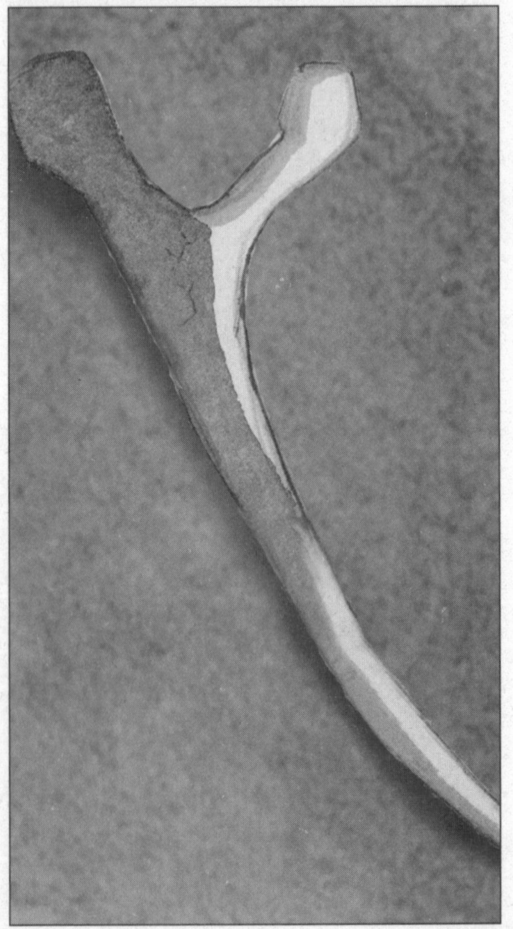

Name ______________________________

21.1

Directions: Have students read each sentence and the two word choices provided for the blank. Tell students to pick the best choice for each sentence and write it in the blank.

1. We ______________________ the food
(hoist·ed, plant·ed)
up the tree.

2. I flipped off my ______________________
(lett·er, lan·tern)
and went to sleep.

3. She was ______________________
(scra**tch**·ing, stuff·ing)
a lar**ge** bug bite.

4. Jack made Nan and Kate an
______________________ to take them
(clatt·er, off·er)
camp·ing.

Directions: Have students read each sentence and the two word choices provided for the blank. Tell students to pick the best choice for each sentence and write it in the blank.

5. Jack had ______________________________
(ma**tch**·es, ma**g**·ic)
for the fire.

6. The ______________________________ robbed
(**g**ents, out·laws)
the sta**g**e·coach!

7. They nabbed Bart ______________________________
(af·ter, to·day)
a long hunt.

8. In the end, Bart shaped up and was
______________________________ with crime.
(start·ing, fin·ished)

3. What tools will they use at the lab to get the bones out of the blocks?

Page ________

4. What did Kate name the T. rex?

Page ________

Name ______________________________

The Big Dig

1. In or·der to get the bones out, the digg·ers have to . . .

   ○ blast a hole in·to the cliff.

   ○ get bigg·er tools soon.

   ○ cut the cliff up in·to lar**ge** blocks of rock.

Pa**ge** __________

2. How will the plas·ter keep the bones safe?

Pa**ge** __________

Directions: Have students reread the story and answer the questions.

Name ____________________

21.3

Dear Family Member,

Your child has been learning to read words with the spellings 'v' *(van)* and 've' *(twelve)* for the sound /v/, and the spellings 'r' *(red)* and 'wr' *(wrist)* for the sound /r/. The words below contain these spellings. Ask your child to cut out the word cards. Show the cards to your child, and have your child read them. Extension: Have your child sort the words into piles according to which spelling is used for the sounds /v/ and /r/.

I'**ve**	vet	shel**ve**s
vast	**wr**ist	**wr**ong
crisp	slee**ve**s	**wr**ap
rich	**wr**ite	twel**ve**

Name ____________________

22.1

1.	switch	swap	swim	swish
2.	cash	catch	cans	caps
3.	stretch	such	straps	stitch
4.	hem	germ	gem	chin
5.	gin·ger	gen·der	gin·seng	grates
6.	ditch	dig·it	date	digs
7.	plunge	lunge	pluck	plug

8.	shall·ot	chipp·er	chall·enge	champ
9.	lunge	large	lake	lunch
10.	sops	solve	sipped	sol·vent
11.	carve	cave	calves	can't
12.	twin	dwell	teen	twelve
13.	ride	write	rip	ripe
14.	wrap	rant	lap	rag
15.	wring	rig	wrist	ramp

Name ______________________________

22.2

Directions: In Part I, have students circle the noun(s) and underline the verb with a squiggly line. In Part II, have students write a question mark, exclamation point, or a period to complete the sentence. In Part III, have students add an adjective and/or a location in order to expand the sentences. In Part IV, students should write the plural form of each noun and also the past tense and –ing form of each verb.

Part I:

Max digs.

1. Kate swims.
2. Frogs hop.
3. The dog barks.
4. Jane ate a hot dog.
5. Those chil·dren run fast.

Part II:

Why is it cold [?]

1. Do you like to shoot bas·kets [ ]
2. I can **wr**ite my name [ ]
3. Can your dog fe**tch** sticks [ ]
4. When is dinn·er [ ]
5. Ca**tch** it [ ]

Part III:

1. My sis·ter runs.

2. Gran bakes.

3. **G**in·**g**er helps.

4. The dogs dig.

5. Max sings.

Name ______________________________

Continued

Part IV:

One paw, five paws

1. One box, three ______________

2. One **wr**ist, five ______________

3. One **g**em, nine ______________

4. One sti**tch**, ten ______________

5. One kiss, three ______________

Root word	***–ed***	***–ing***
jump	jumped	jumping
rub		
pop		
hunt		
nap		

Name ____________________

The Scoop

1. What did the TV man ask Max and Kate?

   ○ Can we see the bone?

   ○ Can we shoot the rocks?

   ○ Can we shoot some film of you?

Page ____________

2. How did Max feel when the T.V. man spoke to him?

____

____

____

____

Page ____________

Directions: Have students reread the story and answer the questions.

3. The man got a close-up of . . .

- ○ the T. rex in the side of the cliff.
- ○ Max and Kate with their forks.
- ○ Ron Fi**tch**, the bone man.

Pa**g**e ___________

4. What did the TV man ask Kate?

____

____

____

____

____

Pa**g**e ___________

Name ______________________________ **PP1**

tch

match

g

germ

ge

large

Directions: Have students trace and copy the spellings and words. Encourage students to say the sounds while writing the letters.

tch

tch

match

g

g

germ

ge

ge

large

Name ______________________________

PP2

Directions: Have students trace and copy the spellings and words. Encourage students to say the sounds while writing the letters.

ve

carve

wr

write

ll

spell

ve

ve

carve

wr

wr

write

ll

ll

spell

Name ______________________________

PP3

Directions: Have students circle the sounds in each word. Then have students count the sounds in the word and write the number in the box. Have students then write the word on the line following the box.

1. **g**em
2. shel**ve**s
3. pi**tch**·er
4. **wr**ecks
5. bul**ge**
6. car**ve**
7. mer**ge**
8. **wr**app·er

9. slee**ve**s

10. filled

11. scatt·er

12. i**tch**

13. ser**ve**

14. lar**g**·er

15. **g**erms

16. blubb·er

Name ______________________________

PP4

Directions: Have students color the boxes that contain words that have 'g' sounded /g/ as in got *in one color and the boxes that contain words that have 'g' sounded /j/ as in* gem *in another color.*

gent·ler	glad	grin
le**g**·end	gift	**g**erm
ma**g**·ic	**g**em	**g**in·**g**er
glass·es	grilled	gar·lic

Name ______________________________

PP5

Directions: Have students color the boxes that contain words that have 'ed' sounded /t/ as in asked in one color and the boxes that contain words that have 'ed' sounded /d/ as in filled in another color.

sparked	hummed	fe**tch**ed
grabbed	crawled	sniffed
wronged	tricked	**wr**apped
ha**tch**ed	cooled	sobbed

Name ____________________

PP6

Sound out the words with the lines un·der them. Is the 'g' sound·ed /g/ as in *got* or /j/ as in *gem*? **Wr**ite the words in the correct space.

gum
glad
dog
← g →
gem
germ

	/g/ as in *got*	/j/ as in *gem*
1. The film had a trag·ic ending. It was so sad!		tragic
2. An ant is a bug.		
3. Mom made a batch of gin·ger snaps.		
4. We have a gas stove in our kitch·en.		
5. Who is your best pal? Rog·er is.		
6. She sent me a get-well card.		

Sound out the words with the lines un·der them. Is the 'g' sound·ed /g/ as in *got* or /j/ as in *gem*? **Wr**ite the words in the correct space.

gum
glad
dog

g

gem
germ

	/g/ as in *got*	/j/ as in *gem*
1. A stone that costs a lot is a gem.		gem
2. She gasped when she saw the snake.		
3. My arms are short·er than my legs.		
4. Scrub your hands to get rid of germs.		
5. A lot of plants are green.		
6. You can·not bend wood. It is rig·id.		

Name ___________________________ **PP7**

The Hike

Directions: Have students write two statements, two questions, and two exclamations based on the illustration.

Name ______________________________ **PP8**

Directions: Have students copy the sentences and circle the noun and draw a squiggly line under the verb in each copied sentence.

1. My **wr**ist bends.

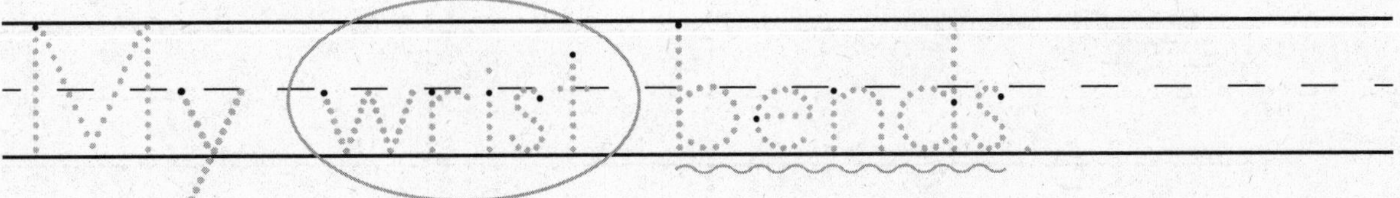

2. The art·ist car**ve**s.

3. The dogs fe**tch**.

4. Its hoo**ve**s clop.

5. His skin i**tch**·es.

6. Mar**ge** sings.

7. Men char**ge**.

8. Her slee**ve** rips.

9. The man stre**tch**·es.

10. Mom **wr**ites.

Name ______________________

PP9

Directions: Have students copy the word onto the left side of the paper, fold it in half, and then write the word from memory on the right side of the paper.

1. ______________________
2. ______________________
3. ______________________
4. ______________________
5. ______________________
6. ______________________
7. ______________________
8. ______________________
9. ______________________
10. ______________________

1. ______________________
2. ______________________
3. ______________________
4. ______________________
5. ______________________
6. ______________________
7. ______________________
8. ______________________
9. ______________________
10. ______________________

Name ____________________

PP10

Cut out the word cards.

stre**tch**	**wr**ing	char**ge**
ner**ve**	twel**ve**	**wr**ote
pi**tch**	lar**g**·est	bar**ge**
ca**tch**	bul**ge**	sol**ve**

Name ______________________________

PP11

Match the word cards to the words on this page.

pitch	solve	wrote
bulge	larg·est	nerve
wring	stretch	barge
charge	catch	twelve

Name ______________________

PP12

Mark the words that are said and **wr**ite them on the lines.

1. a**g**e pa**g**e
2. pi**tch** pa**tch**
3. twel**ve** el**ve**s
4. **wr**ite **wr**ote
5. bar**ge** lar**ge**
6. **g**em jam
7. ki**tch**·en kitt·en
8. Mar**ge** mer**ge**
9. ner**ve** nev·er
10. **wr**ing **wr**ong

Name ______________________________ **PP13**

Yes or no? **Wr**ite *yes* or *no* on the lines.

1. Is ke**tch**·up a game? ____________

2. Is twel**ve** lar**g**·er than nine? ____________

3. Is your **wr**ist part of your leg? ____________

4. Do you sleep in the ki**tch**·en? ____________

5. Do hors·es have hoo**ve**s? ____________

6. Do cats ha**tch** out of eggs? ____________

7. Is a **g**erm lar**g**·er than a bug? ____________

8. Can a bird ca**tch** a bug? ____________

Name ______

PP14

Write the words on the lines.

wrong

catcher

germs

large

ginger

Write the words on the lines.

wrong

catcher

germs

large

ginger

Name ______________________________

PP15

Write the words on the lines.

pitcher

nerve

merge

sleeves

wrap

Write the words on the lines.

pitcher

nerve

merge

sleeves

wrap

Name ______________________________ **PP16**

Mark the words that are said.

1	2
star**ve** starv starf	larg lar**ge** larch
3 rist rrist **wr**ist	**4** ca**g**e cag ca**tch**
5 mach ma**tch** mash	**6** swich swi**tch** swig
7 rong rrong **wr**ong	**8** solf solv sol**ve**

Name ______________________

In the box are six words. **Wr**ite them on the correct lines.

ma**tch**·es	car**ve**	ke**tch**·up
gems	hoo**ve**s	ma**g**·ic

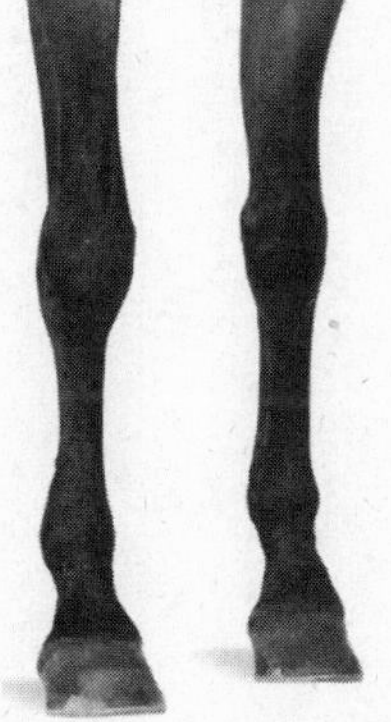

Name ______________________________ **PP18**

Write the words on the correct lines.

1. ma**g**·ic

2. ki**tch**·en

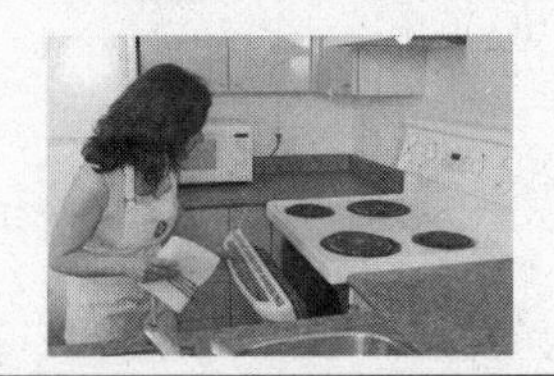

3. ha**tch**

4. lar**ge**

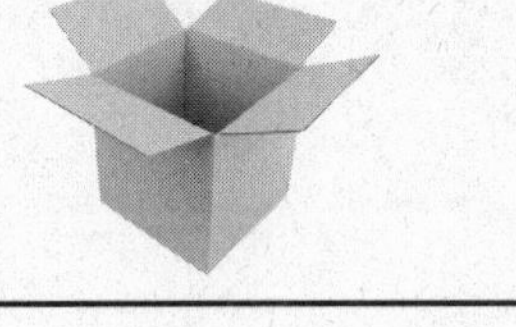

5. twel**ve**

Name ______________________________

PP19

Fill in the ______.

1. He ______________ in·to the pool.

2. We can ______________ the prob·lem.

3. The dog ______________ the stick.

4. The beep·ing sound got on my ______________.

5. ______________ can make you sick.

6. Will you ______________ me a lett·er?

7. What is on the next ______________?

8. Who is the best ______________?

Name ______________________________

PP20

Dear Family Member,

This is a story your child has probably read once, possibly several times, at school. Encourage your child to read the story to you and then talk about it together. The tricky parts in Tricky Words are underlined in gray. Please note that multi-syllable words are divided between syllables with a dot. This dot serves as a cue to assist students in chunking syllables and will be omitted in later units.

Repeated oral reading is an important way to improve reading. It can be fun for your child to repeatedly read this story to a friend, relative, or even a pet.

TAKE HOME

We Are TV Stars

We drove back to Nan's cab·in and got there just in time to see our·sel**ve**s on TV.

The TV man said, "This is Ro**g**·er Fle**tch**·er. I'm stand·ing here in the Bad·lands, where two chil·dren have found the bones of a T. rex."

Then Max and I saw our·sel**ve**s on TV.

"Woo-hoo!" I shout·ed. "We are TV stars!"

Then came the part where the TV man asked Max his name, and Max looked like he was scared of the mike.

"Max, you goof!" I said. "Why did you jump back like that?"

Max just shrugged.

Next the TV man asked me my name.

I said, "I'm Kate." Then I waved.

"Max," said the TV man, "where did you spot the bone?"

Max said, "It was stick·ing out of the side of a cliff."

"What did you use to dig it out?"

"We used our forks!" said Max.

Then we saw the close-up of Max and me with our forks.

"So there you have it!" said the TV man. "I'm Ro**g**·er Fle**tch**·er with a tale of two chil·dren, two forks, and one lar**ge** T. rex!"

Name ______________________________

PP21

Dear Family Member,

This is a story your child has probably read once, possibly several times, at school. Encourage your child to read the story to you and then talk about it together. The tricky parts in Tricky Words are underlined in gray. Please note that multi-syllable words are divided between syllables with a dot. This dot serves as a cue to assist students in chunking syllables and will be omitted in later units.

Repeated oral reading is an important way to improve reading. It can be fun for your child to repeatedly read this story to a friend, relative, or even a pet.

Nan's Book

Max and I and the T. rex were on TV six times. I was glad when it came to an end. Af·ter you smile and wave a fork six times, it gets to be less fun.

One morn·ing, Nan hand·ed me a book and said, "Let's drive to the book shop."

"Nan," I said, "why do you need to get a book at the book shop when you have this one?"

"I just fin·ished that one," Nan said, "I liked it a lot. And it just so happ·ens that the man who **wr**ote it will be at the book shop to·day. I'd like to meet him."

In the car I looked at the book. It said "Dust Up, by Stan Bend·er."

"What sort of book is this?" I asked.

"It's a west·ern," said Nan.

"What's a west·ern?"

"It's a book set out here in the West."

"Is there an out·law in the book like Bart?"

"There's an out·law," said Nan, "but he's not like Bart."

"Why not?"

"He has bad mann·ers!" said Nan.

I looked at the last pa**g**e and saw the pa**g**e num·ber: 305.

"Yikes!" I said. "This is a long book!"

"It is," said Nan. "But it felt short to me be·cause I liked it so much. I was sad when I got to the end!"

I start·ed to look in·side the book, but just then Nan said, "Here we are!"

Name ______________________________

Dear Family Member,

This is a story your child has probably read once, possibly several times, at school. Encourage your child to read the story to you and then talk about it together. The tricky parts in Tricky Words are underlined in gray. Please note that multi-syllable words are divided between syllables with a dot. This dot serves as a cue to assist students in chunking syllables and will be omitted in later units.

Repeated oral reading is an important way to improve reading. It can be fun for your child to repeatedly read this story to a friend, relative, or even a pet.

The Book Shop

In the book shop, there was a big stack of books. Next to the books sat Stan Bend·er, the man who **wr**ote the books. He had a pen in his hand and a big smile on his lips.

"You'd smile too if your book were sell·ing as well as his is!" Nan said.

Nan and I went and stood in line to meet Stan Bend·er.

Nan shook hands with him and said, "I'**ve** got twel**ve** of your books. This one was your best book yet!"

The man smiled and said, "That's sweet of you! I hope you will pick up my next one, too!"

"I will!" said Nan.

Then the man **wr**ote, "Best wish·es, Stan Bend·er," in Nan's book.

"Mis·ter Bend·er," I asked, "how hard was it to **wr**ite that book?"

"Well," he said, "this one was not all that hard. The last one I did was a lot hard·er."

As we got back in the car, I said, "Nan, I'd like to **wr**ite a book."

"What sort of book would it be?" Nan asked.

"Well," I said, "Max and I found the T. rex."

"Yes, you did," said Nan.

"And you and I found that coin."

"Yes," said Nan.

"And we are out here in the West."

"Yes."

"So it could be a bones and coins and west·ern sort of book."

"Why not?" said Nan. "If you **wr**ite it, I will make the pic·tures."

I said, "Shake on it!" Then we shook hands.

Name ____________________

Dear Family Member,

This is a story your child has probably read once, possibly several times, at school. Encourage your child to read the story to you and then talk about it together. The tricky parts in Tricky Words are underlined in gray. Please note that multi-syllable words are divided between syllables with a dot. This dot serves as a cue to assist students in chunking syllables and will be omitted in later units.

Repeated oral reading is an important way to improve reading. It can be fun for your child to repeatedly read this story to a friend, relative, or even a pet.

We Make a Book

When we got back to Nan's, I start·ed to **wr**ite the book. I **wr**ote down all of the cool stuff that happ·ened to me out West. The hard·est part was gett·ing start·ed. Once I got started, it went fast.

Nan helped me pick out good words. Some·times when you **wr**ite, you have to **wr**ite things two or three times to get all of the best words and get them in the best or·der.

Max helped me out, too. He said, "I can help you with spell·ing. I am the best spell·er in my class." Max looked at what I had **wr**itt·en and fixed a lot of spell·ing mis·takes that I had made.

When I had **wr**itt·en the words, Nan got out her brush and start·ed to make the art. It took her a long time. She sent the pic·tures to me three weeks af·ter I went home.

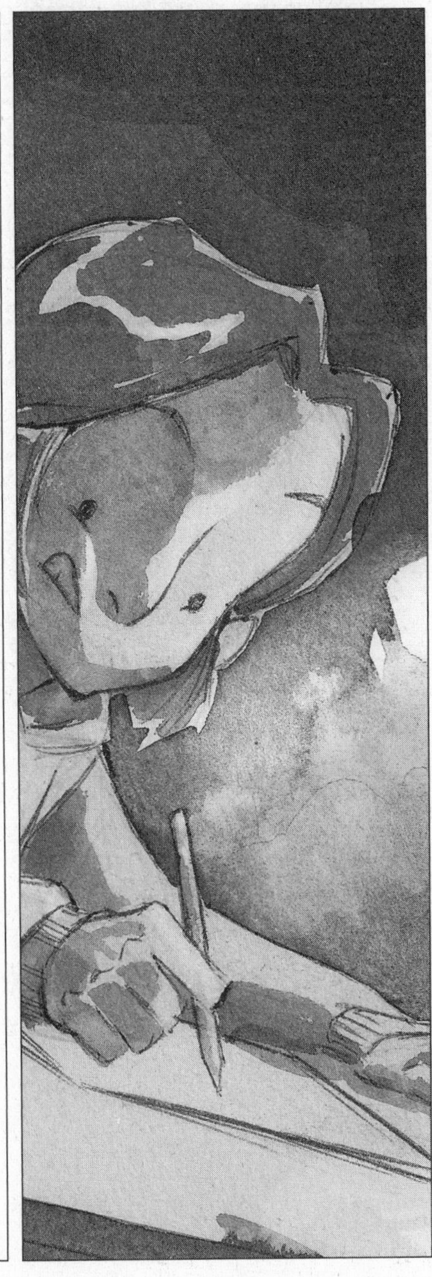

My dad took me and my book to a pal of his to see if he would pub·lish the book.

The man looked at it and said, "This is well-**wr**itt·en! Chil·dren out there will like this book. I'd like to print it!"

I was so glad, I shout·ed, "Yipp·ee!"

The man and his staff got the book all set to pub·lish. Then they sent it to a print·er.

I hope you liked the book.

If you'd like to **wr**ite me a lett·er, you can send it to me at this add·ress:

Kate Skipper
c/o Core Knowledge Foundation
801 East High Street
Charlottesville, Virginia 22902

Name ______________________________

PP24

We Are TV Stars

1. Where were Kate and Max when they saw them·sel**ve**s on TV?

____

____

____

____

Pa**g**e ________

2. What did the TV man ask Kate?

   ○ Where did you spot the coin?

   ○ What's your name?

   ○ Where is your Nan?

Pa**g**e ________

Directions: Have students reread the story and answer the questions.

3. What did the TV man ask Max?

Page

4. Have you ev·er seen your·self or a pal on TV?

Name ______________________________ **PP25**

Nan's Book

1. What sort of book did Nan have?
   - ○ She had a pic·ture book.
   - ○ She had a com·ic book.
   - ○ She had a west·ern.

Page ________

2. How did Nan feel when she got to the end of the book?

____

____

____

____

Page ________

Directions: Have students reread the story and answer the questions.

3. Why did Nan take her book to the book shop?

Page

Directions: In the box, have students illustrate a part of the story and write a caption below.

Name ______________________

PP26

The Book Shop

1. Who is Stan Bend·er?
   - ○ Stan Bend·er **wr**ites west·ern books.
   - ○ Stan Bend·er is Nan's pal.
   - ○ Stan Bend·er is a bone man.

Pa**g**e ________

2. What did Kate ask Mis·ter Bend·er?

Pa**g**e ________

Directions: Have students reread the story and answer the questions.

3. What sort of book would Kate like to make?

Page ________

4. Who will make the pic·tures for Kate's book?

   ○ Kate will make the pic·tures.

   ○ Stan will make the pic·tures.

   ○ Nan will make the pic·tures.

Page ________

Name ________________________________

We Make a Book

1. Who helped Kate with her spell·ing?

Page ________

2. Who made the art for the book?

Page ________

Directions: Have students reread the story and answer the questions.

3. Use the lines to **wr**ite a lett·er to Kate.

Core Knowledge Language Arts

Series Editor-in-Chief
E. D. Hirsch, Jr.

President
Linda Bevilacqua

Editorial Staff
Carolyn Gosse, Senior Editor - Preschool
Khara Turnbull, Materials Development Manager
Michelle L. Warner, Senior Editor - Listening & Learning

Mick Anderson
Robin Blackshire
Maggie Buchanan
Paula Coyner
Sue Fulton
Sara Hunt
Erin Kist
Robin Luecke
Rosie McCormick
Cynthia Peng
Liz Pettit
Ellen Sadler
Deborah Samley
Diane Auger Smith
Sarah Zelinke

Design and Graphics Staff
Scott Ritchie, Creative Director

Kim Berrall
Michael Donegan
Liza Greene
Matt Leech
Bridget Moriarty
Lauren Pack

Consulting Project Management Services
ScribeConcepts.com

Additional Consulting Services
Ang Blanchette
Dorrit Green
Carolyn Pinkerton

Acknowledgments

These materials are the result of the work, advice, and encouragement of numerous individuals over many years. Some of those singled out here already know the depth of our gratitude; others may be surprised to find themselves thanked publicly for help they gave quietly and generously for the sake of the enterprise alone. To helpers named and unnamed we are deeply grateful.

Contributors to Earlier Versions of these Materials

Susan B. Albaugh, Kazuko Ashizawa, Nancy Braier, Kathryn M. Cummings, Michelle De Groot, Diana Espinal, Mary E. Forbes, Michael L. Ford, Ted Hirsch, Danielle Knecht, James K. Lee, Diane Henry Leipzig, Martha G. Mack, Liana Mahoney, Isabel McLean, Steve Morrison, Juliane K. Munson, Elizabeth B. Rasmussen, Laura Tortorelli, Rachael L. Shaw, Sivan B. Sherman, Miriam E. Vidaver, Catherine S. Whittington, Jeannette A. Williams

We would like to extend special recognition to Program Directors Matthew Davis and Souzanne Wright who were instrumental to the early development of this program.

Schools

We are truly grateful to the teachers, students, and administrators of the following schools for their willingness to field test these materials and for their invaluable advice: Capitol View Elementary, Challenge Foundation Academy (IN), Community Academy Public Charter School, Lake Lure Classical Academy, Lepanto Elementary School, New Holland Core Knowledge Academy, Paramount School of Excellence, Pioneer Challenge Foundation Academy, New York City PS 26R (The Carteret School), PS 30X (Wilton School), PS 50X (Clara Barton School), PS 96Q, PS 102X (Joseph O. Loretan), PS 104Q (The Bays Water), PS 214K (Michael Friedsam), PS 223Q (Lyndon B. Johnson School), PS 308K (Clara Cardwell), PS 333Q (Goldie Maple Academy), Sequoyah Elementary School, South Shore Charter Public School, Spartanburg Charter School, Steed Elementary School, Thomas Jefferson Classical Academy, Three Oaks Elementary, West Manor Elementary.

And a special thanks to the CKLA Pilot Coordinators Anita Henderson, Yasmin Lugo-Hernandez, and Susan Smith, whose suggestions and day-to-day support to teachers using these materials in their classrooms was critical.

Credits

Every effort has been taken to trace and acknowledge copyrights. The editors tender their apologies for any accidental infringement where copyright has proved untraceable. They would be pleased to insert the appropriate acknowledgment in any subsequent edition of this publication. Trademarks and trade names are shown in this publication for illustrative purposes only and are the property of their respective owners. The references to trademarks and trade names given herein do not affect their validity.

All photographs are used under license from Shutterstock, Inc. unless otherwise noted.

Illustrators and Image Sources

Cover: Shutterstock; Title Page: Shutterstock; Take Home Icon: Core Knowledge Staff; 1.2: Shutterstock; 2.1: Shutterstock; 3.3: Jacob Wyatt; 7.1: Jacob Wyatt; 8.3: Jacob Wyatt; 10.2: Jacob Wyatt; 14.4: Jacob Wyatt; 18.2: Jacob Wyatt; 20.3: Jacob Wyatt; PP7: Jacob Wyatt; PP17: Shutterstock; PP18: Shutterstock; PP20: Jacob Wyatt; PP21: Jacob Wyatt; PP22: Jacob Wyatt; PP23: Jacob Wyatt

Regarding the Shutterstock items listed above, please note: "No person or entity shall falsely represent, expressly or by way of reasonable implication, that the content herein was created by that person or entity, or any person other than the copyright holder(s) of that content."